Mushroom for dinner

Story by Beverley Randell

Illustrated by Isabel Lowe

Father Bear came home and said,
"Look! **No** mushrooms!
I did not find **one**!
I'm going fishing."

"I'm good at finding mushrooms,"
said Baby Bear.
"I will go and get some."

Baby Bear went
uphill and downhill
looking for mushrooms.
He went on and on.

"Where are the mushrooms?"
he said.
"Where **are** they?"

"I can't see **one** mushroom,"
said Baby Bear.

He said to a rabbit,
"Will you help me
find some mushrooms?"

But the rabbit ran away.

"I will have to find
the mushrooms
by **myself**,"
said Baby Bear.
"I will climb
up this tree
to have a look."

9

Baby Bear climbed the tree.

"I can **see** some!" he said.

"I can see a ring of mushrooms.
Good. I will go and get some."

Baby Bear ran to get
the big white mushrooms.

He went home
with the basket of mushrooms.
"Here you are," he said. "Look!"

"Thank you, Baby Bear,"
said Mother Bear.
"They are **beautiful** mushrooms.
You are a clever little bear."

And the three bears all had
fish and **mushrooms** for dinner.